100s of Amish Hints

Publications International, Ltd.

Barbara R. Duncan grew up on a farm in central Pennsylvania and has a Ph.D. in folklore and folklife from the University of Pennsylvania. This award-winning writer and musician has written several books, including *Amish Folk Medicine* and *Living Stories of the Cherokee*. She lives in the Smoky Mountains of North Carolina, where she has collected local stories and folklore for more than 25 years.

Cover Illustration: Erin Burke

Interior Illustrations: Clipart.com, Fotosearch, Steven Noble

Louis Weber, CEO
Publications International, Ltd.
8140 Lehigh Avenue
Morton Grove, Illinois 60053

ISBN-13: 978-1-4508-2378-4
ISBN-10: 1-4508-2378-5

Manufactured in China.

8 7 6 5 4 3 2 1

CONTENTS

PRACTICAL WISDOM TO LIVE BY

"The hurrieder I go, the behinder I get."
—Amish proverb

Amish people live simple, frugal, hard-working lives, focused on God and the community. Their down-to-earth lifestyle includes many practical solutions to running a household—solutions even those of us who use electricity and modern appliances can adopt. You can save money and live a more natural life following their lead.

This book includes more than 200 time-honored hints. Learn how to substitute products that you already have on your shelves for costly store-bought items. There are many quick and easy, cost-effective recipes for everything from cleaning products to macaroni and cheese. If you garden, learn to save seeds and start your own plants and to use natural pest control. The chapter on staying healthy and treating illness provides safe and natural ways to deal with common health problems, from anxiety to wounds. There are even hints for personal care, from toothbrushing to weight loss.

With *100s of Amish Hints,* you, too, can learn to "make do" like the Amish!

KITCHEN ORGANIZATION AND COOKING

"Kissing don't last. Cooking do."
—Amish proverb

The kitchen is the heart of the Amish home, where family, friends, and visitors gather to eat at the kitchen table. Amish kitchens don't have electricity, but with a paring knife, a wood or gas stove, and helping hands, Amish families create bountiful meals. The ingredients come mostly from their gardens and farms. They cook from scratch, and they make do with what they have. If they can't afford it, then they do without it.

WASTE NOT, WANT NOT

Nothing in an Amish kitchen or on an Amish farm goes to waste. Here are some ways to make the most of what you've stocked in your own larder.

Versatile broth. Buy chicken, pork, or beef with bones instead of boneless cuts. Make a meal with them, but don't throw out the bones afterward. Boil the bones for about 90 minutes in a large pot of water to which has been added a clove of garlic, an onion, and a handful of carrots and celery. Strain out the bones, being careful to catch any small pieces, and use the stock as a base for any soup recipe.

Droop for soup. Even vegetables that are starting to droop will be fine in a soup. Adding a dash of parsley or other fresh or dried herbs will enhance the flavor.

Rejuvenate vegetables. To bring wilted lettuce or celery to life, place them in a pan of cold water with a peeled raw potato in it.

No end to cheese. Don't throw out the hard ends of cheese. Grate them, then add them to salads, soups, or chili. Or, freeze them for later use.

BAKING AND COOKING HINTS

- When adding fruits, nuts, or raisins to batter, roll them in flour first. This will keep them from clumping together, and they will be distributed more evenly throughout the batter and the finished cake or muffins.

- When baking chocolate cake, dust the greased cake pan with cocoa instead of white flour. This adds chocolate flavor and a nice chocolate color to the outside of the cake.

- You can make a streusel coffee cake out of any plain yellow cake mix. Make the batter as directed on the package. In a separate bowl, mix 1 stick softened butter with 1 cup brown sugar, ⅔ cup flour, and 1 teaspoon cinnamon. Combine until the texture is crumbly. Sprinkle on the cake batter and bake as usual. This is good when baked in a 9×13 pan.

- Before frying or sautéing, sprinkle ¼ teaspoon salt into the pan to reduce splattering outside the pan.

Amish Bread

Homemade bread is part of every Amish meal. Traditionally, baking is done on Fridays. Baking once a week can be very economical—you only have to heat your oven once, and you can make 2 or 3 loaves of bread in the same time it would take to make one. Wrap up the breads carefully, and they will stay fresh. You can even slice a loaf and freeze it for a few days.

- Before icing a layer cake, cut strips of waxed paper about 2 inches wide and put them on the platter so they form an edge around the outside of the cake. When you are done frosting, just pull the strips out and dispose of them. The platter will be clean, and the cake will look neat and finished.
- Instead of frosting a bundt cake, sprinkle it with confectioners' sugar. Put about ¾ cup confectioners' sugar in a sifter and sift over the top of the cake.
- If you are going to cream together butter and sugar, first rinse the bowl with boiling water. They will cream faster.
- If you are cutting butter into flour to make piecrust or pastry, first rinse the bowl with ice water. This will make the butter blend more uniformly with the flour, without melting first.
- Boil rice in chicken broth instead of water to make it more nutritious and flavorful. Or, use half water and half chicken broth.
- Buy cheese in bulk, and use a vegetable peeler to make uniform slices for snacks. Turn the block of cheese on its side and use the peeler along the edges to make shreds of cheese for sprinkling on soups and pasta or other garnishes. This works best if the cheese is cold.
- To get more juice from a fresh lemon, place the lemon in a cup of hot water for about five minutes. Then squeeze as usual.

- When muffins are done, remove from oven and set the pan immediately on a wet dish towel. This will make the muffins slide out of the pans more easily.

- When adding water to your piecrust, use ice water to keep the crust from getting tough.

- To make an attractive browned piecrust, before baking use a pastry brush to apply 1–2 tablespoons milk or cream. Sprinkle with 1–2 tablespoons sugar.

- To glaze your piecrust, beat 1 whole egg or just the egg white with 1–2 teaspoons water. Brush on before baking.

- Save the wrappers from sticks of butter or margarine and keep in freezer. Take out and use to grease cookie sheets or cake pans. There will be enough butter left on the papers to grease your pans.

CLEVER SUBSTITUTIONS

Just because you don't have the ingredients a recipe calls for doesn't mean you have to rush out and buy them. Here's how to create substitutions from your own cupboard.

- When a recipe calls for buttermilk, make a quick substitute by stirring 1 tablespoon vinegar into 1 cup milk. Let it sit for about five minutes, until it begins to thicken. The true buttermilk tang may be missing, but this works just fine as a substitute.

- If someone is allergic to eggs or you've run out of them, substitute 3 tablespoons soft or silken tofu for every egg in pie and custard recipes.
- Substitute ⅓ cup applesauce for every egg in muffin recipes.
- Lemon and vinegar can be used interchangeably. The taste will be a little different, but the result will be the same.
- In baking, you can substitute ⅓ cup applesauce for every ⅓ cup of oil. This works best in bread and muffin recipes.
- For 1 cup of honey, substitute ¾ cup maple syrup plus ½ cup white sugar.
- To reduce fat and cholesterol in a recipe, use 2 egg whites instead of 1 egg.
- Instead of sour cream, use the same amount of plain yogurt in a recipe. It is cheaper and has fewer calories.
- For 1 cup heavy cream, substitute ⅔ cup whole milk plus ⅓ cup melted, unsalted butter. *Note*: You will not be able to whip this for whipped cream.

HOMEMADE VIRTUES

The Amish don't shun store-bought food products, but they use them sparingly. Frugal by creed, they know that homemade items are usually the least expensive—and the most tasty! Here are some easy recipes for products you use every day.

Salad Dressing. Basic salad dressing is a combination of 1 part vinegar (any kind) mixed with 3 parts oil (olive oil is a flavorful and healthy choice). A standard amount is ¾ cup oil and ¼ cup vinegar. Add salt and pepper, and fresh or dried herbs to taste; some like a little bit of sugar in the dressing, too. Shake well and store in the refrigerator.

Raspberry Vinegar

Put 2 cups apple cider vinegar or white vinegar in a stainless steel, glass, or enamel pan. Add 2 cups fresh or frozen raspberries and ½ cup sugar. Bring to boil, then reduce heat and simmer for about 10 minutes. Pour vinegar through a strainer and into a glass pint jar for storage. This vinegar will keep in the refrigerator for several months.

Tip: Using white vinegar will make a prettier red color for your vinegar.

- For Italian dressing, add 1 teaspoon each oregano and basil, 1 clove crushed garlic, salt, and pepper.
- For tarragon vinaigrette, add 1 tablespoon dried tarragon and a pinch of sugar.
- For creamy vinaigrette, add heavy cream to either of the above.
- For unique, low-cost, and low-calorie heart-healthy salad dressings, start by making your own flavored vinegars. Sprinkle

them on salads with 1 teaspoon olive oil. To make raspberry vinegar, use the recipe on page 11. *Tip:* Purchase vinegar by the gallon to save.

White sauce. Instead of buying cans of soup or prepackaged meals, make your own white sauce to use for macaroni and cheese, green bean casserole, and creamy soups. It takes just a few simple ingredients and about 15 minutes of your time.

- Melt 2 tablespoons butter in a saucepan.
- Stir in 2 tablespoons flour; continue stirring for a few minutes, but don't allow it to brown.
- Pour in 1 cup milk and stir with a whisk until mixture comes to a boil.
- Continue to stir constantly until thickened, 1–2 minutes.This requires your attention—don't multitask or the white sauce could scorch.
- Remove from heat.

Variations with white sauce:

Macaroni and cheese. Cook 8 ounces macaroni and drain. To the white sauce, add 8 ounces grated cheddar cheese, salt, and pepper. Combine cheese sauce with cooked macaroni and serve.

Or put the mixture in a greased 8×8 (2-quart) baking dish; bake at 350 degrees Fahrenheit for 30 minutes.

Cream of mushroom sauce for green bean casserole. Cook 2 to 3 cups green beans; drain. To the white sauce, add 1 cup sautéed mushrooms, salt, and pepper. Mix with sauce, put mixture in greased baking dish, top with bread crumbs, and bake 30 minutes.

Cream of broccoli soup: Cook 2 to 3 cups broccoli, drain, and process in blender until chopped fine. Mix 1 cup grated cheese into the white sauce; add broccoli, and salt and pepper to taste. Reheat and serve. Be careful not to scorch the soup.

Creamy potato soup. Boil 2 to 3 cups peeled and chopped potatoes with a little salt and pepper.

Amish Recipe for a Happy Marriage

3 cups love
2 cups warmth
1 cup forgiveness
1 cup friends
4 spoons of hope
2 spoons of tenderness
1 pint of faith
1 barrel of laughter

1. Combine warmth and love.
2. Mix thoroughly with tenderness.
3. Add forgiveness.
4. Blend with friends and hope, and sprinkle with remaining tenderness.
5. Stir with faith and laughter. Bake with sunshine, and serve daily in generous helpings.

Drain and mash. Sauté ½ small chopped white onion and 1 clove minced garlic. Mix together all the ingredients, then add to the white sauce.

FABULOUS FIXES

Amish kitchen know-how resolves minor cooking problems and averts major disasters. These tips and tricks of the trade will come to the rescue when you need them.

- Tenderize tough cuts of meat. The least expensive cuts of meat are also usually the toughest. Use a dull knife to beat the meat in a crisscross pattern. Then marinate the meat in 4 tablespoons soy sauce or vinegar for several hours.
- Prevent eggs from cracking. Add 2 tablespoons vinegar to the water when cooking hard-boiled eggs.
- Keep egg whites white. Add 1 teaspoon vinegar to the water when poaching eggs to keep the whites well formed.
- Restore wilted vegetables' firmness by soaking them in 1 quart cold water mixed with 2 tablespoons vinegar.
- If you've added too much salt to your dish, add 1 teaspoon vinegar and 1 teaspoon sugar. Or, peel a raw potato and add it to the dish to absorb the salt.
- No more tears! Peel onions underwater to keep from crying when you cut or dice them.

- If your eggs have passed their freshness date, here's a test to determine if they are fresh. Mix thoroughly about 3 tablespoons salt into 1 pint cold water. Put the salted water into a small pan, so there is enough water to cover the eggs (about four inches.) Place an egg gently in the pan. If it sinks it's fresh. If it floats, the egg is turning bad and should be thrown out.

- If brown sugar has hardened, put a slice of bread and the hard sugar into a sealed plastic bag. Leave overnight. The next day, the moisture from the bread will be absorbed into the brown sugar, making it soft enough to measure and use. Discard the piece of bread and seal the brown sugar tightly in its bag.

- Keep salt flowing freely by adding a few grains of rice to the saltshaker. The rice absorbs moisture.

- To prevent potatoes or pasta from boiling over, add 1 tablespoon butter or olive oil to the water. It will keep them from sticking, too!

PRESERVE AND PROTECT

The Amish have learned how to keep food fresh as long as possible, and they preserve produce for use during the long winter months when fresh fruit and vegetables aren't available. This is a thrify and healthful practice. You can benefit, too, by following these tips.

- Buy produce in quantity from your local farmer's market or grocery store. Then freeze, can, or dry it—just like the Amish do with produce from their farms and gardens. Drying fruits intensifies their flavor and turns them into delicious snacks. Turning fruit into jelly or jam preserves the fruit in a delicious form that can be used year-round.
- When you make soup, double or triple the amount and freeze it for later use. This saves both time and energy.
- Buy staples like flour in the largest quantity possible. Store in glass jars or hard plastic containers in a cool, dry place away from light to help them last.
- If you have a cellar, use it to store apples, potatoes, onions, and other root vegetables. These do best in a cool, dark, dry environment.
- Keep onions and garlic separate from potatoes so that the flavors don't transfer.

Making Apple Butter

The night before apple butter making, the Amish get together for the "schnitzing" or cutting of the apples. The apple butter must boil but not burn, so it has to be carefully tended. It can take most of a day to cook down the apples into a thick, delicious spread for homemade bread. They even like to eat it combined with cottage cheese—*schmierkase*—an acquired Amish taste. Originally flavored with sassafras from the woods and fencerows, apple butter tastes "wonderful good" flavored with cinnamon, cloves, or even anise.

- Check vegetables and fruits weekly for bad spots. Remove any that you find. One rotten apple spoils the barrel, says the adage—and it is true.

- If you have an attic, hang herbs and flowers to dry there. The heat of the house rises to the attic, keeping it dry and warm—the perfect environment for drying herbs and flowers.

- Hang herbs until they are thoroughly dry, then store them in glass containers until ready to crumble and use.

- When drying flowers, hang them in a well-ventilated place out of the sunshine. Sun will fade their colors. When dry, place in vases or wreaths to brighten the winter.

- If bananas are turning brown on the outside, preserve them to use later in baking. Remove peels and mash them together. Measure the amount of banana pulp, then freeze it in a plastic bag or bowl. Mark the amount on the outside so you know how much you have.

- When slicing apples for pie or applesauce, sprinkle with fresh lemon juice to keep them from turning brown.

CLEAN KITCHEN AND COOK

- Place about ¼ cup activated charcoal in a small bowl and put in refrigerator to absorb odors.

- Pour vanilla on a cotton ball, put in a small bowl, and keep in refrigerator to eliminate unpleasant odors.

- To keep your cookbook fresh, turn to the recipe you're using, and then slide the cookbook into a large plastic bag.
- To remove cooking odors, boil ¼ cup vinegar or orange or lemon peels in a pan of water.
- To remove onion odors from hands, rub with vinegar.
- To remove pesticides from produce, wash with a solution of 1 quart lukewarm water and 1 tablespoon baking soda. Then rinse with clear, running water.
- Keep a pump bottle with vinegar next to the sink, and use it after handling raw meat or eggs, or just to wash thoroughly.
- To freshen and clean dishcloths and sponges, soak in 1 quart warm water and 4 tablespoons baking soda.
- To freshen the refrigerator, put an open box of baking soda in it; change the box every three months. Or, wipe down walls and shelves with vinegar and water.
- To deodorize plastic containers, soak in a solution of 1 quart warm water and 4 tablespoons baking soda. You can also wipe them out with a cloth soaked in vinegar. Rinse with clear water and let air dry.
- To clean coffeemakers and tea kettles, run a potful of vinegar through the cycle, then follow with a pot of water. Or, scrub with baking soda on a damp sponge, then rinse.
- To clean tea and coffee stains out of mugs, put some baking soda on a damp sponge and use it to scrub the stains away;

wash and rinse. Or, make a paste with equal amounts salt and vinegar and scrub stains away, wash and rinse.

- To clean copper-bottomed pots, rub the bottom with salt or salt and vinegar. Wash with regular detergent and dry.

- To keep moths and bugs out of the pantry, put bay leaves in cupboards, pantry, and flour bins. Buy bay leaves in large quantities to make this economical.

- To deodorize garbage cans and recycling containers, wash them out with a solution made with 1 cup baking soda and 1 gallon water. Sprinkle fresh baking soda in bottom of the can every time you change the garbage bag. After rinsing glass and plastic containers for recycling, sprinkle baking soda directly on them to eliminate odors.

The Plain People

Amish women make their own clothing from solid-colored cloth, and their houses have no hex signs or gingerbread porch trim. Their windows often have no curtains. They live in a way that sets them apart from the world because they believe that's how best to follow God. They rejoice in God's creation, and their yards are full of marigolds, roses, nasturtiums, dahlias, and daylilies. A damp corner behind the house holds apple mint and spearmint that yield up their fragrances. The quilts on their clotheslines exhibit a glory of geometric shapes and colors. And every day their perfectly crimped pies, carefully canned pickles, and lightly browned bread sustain their families with love and utilitarian beauty.

- To remove cooking odors, put 4 cups nonchlorinated water into a stainless steel or glass pan. Add 10 drops oil of peppermint or oil of spearmint. (You can also use peppermint extract from the baking section of your grocery store.) Bring to a boil, then simmer until pan is almost dry.

- To clean and deodorize drains the nontoxic way, use the natural foaming reaction of vinegar and baking soda. This solution is not harmful to your septic system. Put ½ cup baking soda in drain and add ½ cup vinegar. Let gurgle for 15 minutes, then flush with hot running water for a few minutes. If water is still draining slowly, repeat.

- Smother minor kitchen fires with salt, flour, or baking soda. Baking soda gives off carbon dioxide when heated, which helps extinguish flames even faster.

- When dishtowels wear out, cut them up to use for rags for dusting and polishing.

- Save the glass jars that food comes in. Wash thoroughly, dry, and store, then use to hold food leftovers, homemade cleaning supplies, and other liquids. Label the contents. **Caution:** Do not use for freezing or canning.

**"Don't hurry, don't worry.
Do your best and leave the rest."
—Amish proverb**

HOUSE CLEANING AND LAUNDRY

"Let us pray not for lighter burdens but for stronger backs."
—Amish proverb

Amish parents raise large families without electricity or labor-saving appliances. They follow a yearly, weekly, and daily rhythm that orders their lives and chores. Monday is washday, Friday is for baking, Sunday is for church and then rest. Amish homes and yards are simple, and their dedicated labor creates an orderliness that is beautiful.

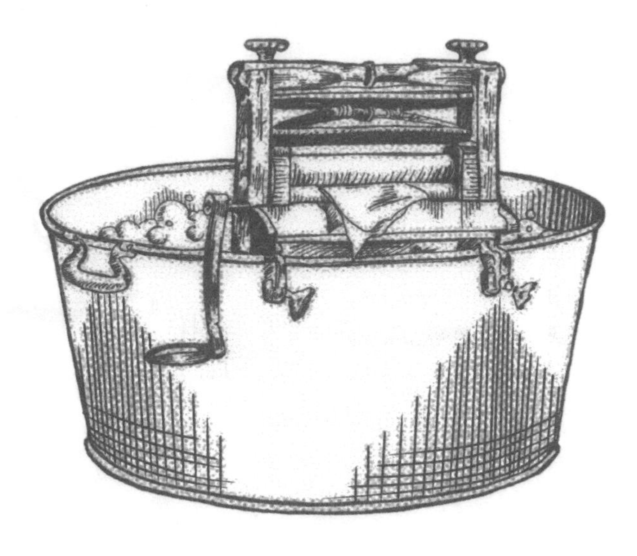

CLEANING

- For sparkling windows, mix ⅓ cup vinegar with 1 quart water. Put the solution in a bucket or a squirt bottle. Apply to windows, then wipe down excess water with a squeegee if desired. Rub windows with old newspaper to dry and polish.
- Get rid of black scuff marks on the floor by rubbing them with baby oil. Then wash the area with soap and water so it won't be slippery.
- Remove chewing gum from hair or carpet by rubbing it with peanut butter. The peanut butter will combine with and soften the chewing gum. Then you can separate the mixture from the strands of hair or from the nap of the carpet. Remove the mixture completely: For hair, shampoo and rinse. For carpet, if a spot remains, use a spot remover or a detergent like Dawn for dishes that removes grease. Rub the spot clean and then rub with plain hot water.
- Whether carpet odor is caused by baby messes, pet accidents, or spills, baking soda is the odor-eating remedy. Sprinkle some baking soda on the carpet, leave it for at least 30 minutes—but longer

Cinnamon Carpet Freshener

For a fresh cinnamon scent, add 2 tablespoons cinnamon to a small box of baking soda. Shake and let sit overnight. Sprinkle it on the carpet and let it sit overnight. Sweep (or vacuum) in the morning.

or even overnight if you wish. Sweep (or vacuum) up the soda and discard.

- To solve mildew problems, mix ¼ cup vinegar, ¼ cup liquid bleach, and 1 quart water in a bucket. Soak a cleaning cloth in the mixture, and apply it liberally to the mildewed area. Leave the cloth on the mildew for about 30 minutes.
- To prevent mildew from growing, wash the area with a mixture of water and vinegar. Use about ½ cup vinegar to 2 quarts water.

Vinegar

In an Amish household, vinegar is used for everything from pickling to personal hygiene. Apple cider vinegar is used most often because the Amish make it themselves. In these recipes and remedies, you can use white vinegar, distilled vinegar, or apple cider vinegar unless one type is specified. Organic apple cider vinegar is the best. It may develop a cloudy mass, called "mother of vinegar," in the bottom after it is opened, but it is not harmful.

Vinegar is used to make the Amish's renowned sauerkraut, many kinds of pickles, and other favorite dishes like "chow chow," a relish. Dishes made with vinegar are so popular that some say an Amish meal is not complete unless it includes "seven sweets and seven sours."

Vinegar is not expensive—and it will be even cheaper if you buy it by the gallon.

BATHROOM

- To clean sinks, tubs, and other surfaces, including fiberglass and tile, sprinkle with baking soda and rub with a damp sponge. Wipe, then rinse with warm water.
- To disinfect bathroom surfaces, add 1 tablespoon tea tree or orange essential oil to 1 quart warm water. Put the mixture in a spray bottle. Shake well, then spray and wipe surfaces. These oils have disinfectant properties and will leave a pleasant scent.
- Clean grout by applying full-strength vinegar and letting it sit for five minutes. Scrub with an old toothbrush, then rinse.
- Mix 1 cup white vinegar, ½ cup baking soda, and 1 cup ammonia in 1 gallon warm water to make a tile-cleaning solution.
- Clean toilet bowl by pouring 3 cups distilled white vinegar into it. Let sit for several hours, scrub, and flush.
- Put full-strength white vinegar in a spray bottle and use to disinfect countertops and doorknobs, as well as the surfaces around the toilet.

FLOORS

- For general cleaning of floors, woodwork, walls, and furniture, combine ¼ cup vinegar and 1 tablespoon liquid soap with 1 gallon warm water. Mop or hand wash area, rinse with clean warm water, and air dry.

- Add ½ cup baking soda to a bucket of warm water and mop vinyl, linoleum, or tile floors. Do not use on hardwood floors.
- Put 1 tablespoon essential oil—tea tree oil or orange oil work well—and 1 tablespoon liquid soap in a large bucket of hot water. Stir with mop and use on floors.
- You can also use your mixture of essential oil and water in a spray bottle to spray on a spot or spill. Wipe up with a clean cloth or damp mop.
- For a quick floor cleanup, mix together 1 cup water, 1 cup white vinegar, 1 cup rubbing alcohol, and a few drops of liquid soap. Spray on the floor and mop immediately.
- To sweep without stirring up dust, put a few drops of olive oil or baby oil on the broom before sweeping.

WALLS

- In a bucket, make a solution of 1 gallon warm water, 1 cup ammonia, ½ cup vinegar, and ¼ cup baking soda. Mix and apply with a rag or mop to clean walls and woodwork.
- For crayon marks, stains, and scuff marks: Put some baking soda on a sponge and rub directly on the marks. Wipe with warm water.

POLISHING METALS

- To clean and polish silver without using expensive, toxic products, all you need are a potato, baking powder, and "elbow grease." Cut the potato into quarters. Put

1 tablespoon baking powder in a small bowl. Dip the cut side of the potato into the baking powder, then rub hard and fast (use "elbow grease") on the silver you want to clean for 30 to 60 seconds. Your silver will shine like a mirror.

- **Caution:** When you are done, be sure to throw away the potato and any unused baking powder left in the little bowl. They will look gray because the tarnish you removed from the silver includes oxidized metal. This can be harmful if eaten.

- **Tip:** If you're polishing a lot of silver, cut a little sliver out of the side of the potato where your thumb will be holding it. This will give you a better grip.

To clean and polish brass, copper, or pewter, make a paste of equal amounts of white vinegar and table salt. Put the paste onto the metal, scrub, and rinse.

LAUNDRY AND CLOTHING

Amish women don't use washing machines; instead, they use hand power to get their laundry washed, rinsed, and dried. First they put the clothes in a tub of warm water, adding homemade lye soap and scrubbing the clothes on a washboard. Then they run the clothes through a hand-operated wringer to remove excess water. Next comes the rinse—in a large tub of clean water—and another trip through the wringer. Laundry is hung to dry on clotheslines outdoors, even in the winter.

The following tips are adapted for modern washing machines and dryers powered by electricity and gas.

- To deodorize laundry, add ½ cup baking soda to the rinse cycle. This will make your clothes, sheets, and towels smell as fresh as if you hung them outdoors.

- If clothes have strong body odor or begin to smell musty, add ½ cup baking soda to the wash water to deodorize.

- To whiten cotton fabric, pour 1 gallon hot water into a bucket or a pan large enough to hold the items you want to clean. Add ½ cup liquid dishwashing detergent and ½ cup liquid bleach. Add cottons and soak 30 minutes. Put cottons in the washing machine and wash according to your usual method. You can also use this solution and soaking method for synthetic fabric, but you may not need to soak as long.

- To keep clothes smelling fresh and keep their colors bright, add 1 cup white vinegar to the rinse cycle.

Baking Soda

Baking soda is more than just an ingredient that makes baked goods rise. It whitens, cleans, and deodorizes, too. The Amish use it in cooking, for cleaning, and for personal hygiene. Baking soda releases carbon dioxide when it is heated, and the bubbles that it creates cause baked goods to rise and also make it a great cleaner.

- To whiten any fabric, soak in a gallon of water mixed with ½ cup chlorine bleach and ½ cup baking soda. The baking soda makes the bleach more effective, so you will need less of the harsh chemical.

- Vinegar can also help whiten fabrics. Bring a large pot of water to a boil and then add 1 cup white vinegar. Add stained white clothing and bring back to a boil. Turn off heat. Let soak overnight, then wash as usual.

- Scorch marks—the bane of anyone who irons—don't have to destroy your white clothes. Spray them with full-strength peroxide, cover with a white cloth, and iron again. Like magic, the scorch marks should disappear.

STAINS

- For blood stains, pour full-strength peroxide on the stain. It will bubble away the stain. Let sit for about 30 minutes, then wash in cold water.

- To remove ballpoint pen marks, use full-strength rubbing alcohol. Pour alcohol on the pen mark and let set about 30 minutes. If the stain does not disappear, repeat and rub gently. Wash as usual.

- To remove grease spots on fabric, use Dawn liquid dishwashing detergent. Pour full strength on the spot and let sit about 30 minutes. Rub gently, then wash as usual.

- Say good-bye to condiment stains like those from mustard, ketchup, and barbecue sauce, by rubbing vinegar into them before washing.

- To remove blackberry, blueberry, and other berry stains, soak in equal parts milk and vinegar until stain disappears. Then wash in cold water.

SACHETS AND INSECT REPELLENTS

These all-natural sachets will keep your clothes smelling fresh and fragrant—and they make lovely gifts. As a bonus, they will also repel moths and insects, so they'll leave your clothes alone.

- Use an awl or ice pick to make holes all over the peel on the outside of an orange, spacing the holes about ⅛ to ¼ inch apart. Insert whole cloves into all the holes, being careful not to split the skin in-between. Roll the orange in 1 tablespoon cinnamon. Then roll in 1 tablespoon ground orrisroot. (You can skip the orrisroot step, but the orange will shrivel in about a month. The orrisroot acts as a natural preservative so the orange will last longer.)Tie up the orange in netting or cheesecloth, and hang it in your closet.
- Another way to use cloves is to fill small cloth bags with them or just put the cloves directly into the pockets of woolen coats, in bags with sweaters, or in drawers during the wintertime.
- Sew a small bag (about 2×2-inch square or larger) out of scraps of medium to lightweight material that are left over from other projects. Fill with dried herbs like peppermint or lavender and sew shut. Place in drawers between layers of clothing or in closets. To refresh, take out and sprinkle with

rubbing alcohol. It will dry quickly, and you can place it back in the drawer.

- You can also make sachets containing other herbs and spices. Sew several small bags as described above. Mix well 4 ounces orrisroot with 1 ounce each powdered cloves, cinnamon, nutmeg, and mace. Fill bags and sew shut.
- Fill small bags with cedar shavings and keep in drawers and closets to repel moths.
- Put a block of red cedar wood in drawers and closets to repel moths. When the block begins to lose its scent, refresh it by rubbing it lightly with sandpaper.

FURNITURE AND WOOD

Natural furniture polish will keep your wood furniture clean, lubricated, and shiny, while manufactured products can ruin wood with chemicals.

Furniture polish. Put 1 pint warm nonchlorinated water, 1 tablespoon vinegar, and 1 tablespoon oil—either olive, cedar, orange, or lemon—into a glass pint jar with lid and shake well. Use a soft, dry cloth to wipe off furniture with this mixture, then polish with another soft dry cloth. Shake well before each use.

Antique furniture polish. Put ½ cup linseed oil, ½ cup vinegar, and 2 cups turpentine into a 1-quart jar and shake well.

Before using, wipe furniture with a damp cloth. Then rub a small amount of this polish onto the furniture with a rag. Polish with a soft dry cloth.

Cleaning solution for wood paneling. Mix 1 quart warm water with ½ cup olive oil and 1 cup white vinegar. Apply to paneling with mop or soft cloth. Rinse with warm water and allow to air dry.

Polish for wood floors. Mix together 1 cup linseed oil, 1 cup turpentine, and 1 cup vinegar. Shake well before using.

BABY ITEMS

- To safely remove odors from baby bottles, fill them with warm water and 1 teaspoon baking soda. Shake for 10 seconds or so, then rinse and wash.
- To deodorize bottles and nipples, use a solution of 1 quart warm water mixed with 4 tablespoons baking soda. Fill the bottles with the solution, and soak them overnight. Fill a small bowl with the leftover solution, and use it to soak the nipples and rings. Then rinse and clean as usual.
- Sprinkle baking soda directly on a damp sponge, then use to clean playpen, high chair, car seat, stroller, or changing table. Wipe off thoroughly with warm water on warm sponge or rag and let dry.

- To clean and deodorize baby toys, soak in a solution of 4 tablespoons baking soda to 1 quart warm water. Wash, rinse, and let dry.
- To clean and deodorize baby's stuffed animals, sprinkle them with baking soda. Let sit for fifteen minutes, then brush off thoroughly. This will freshen up baby's favorite toys that can't be washed in the washing machine. No harmful residues are left.
- Clean and disinfect board books and vinyl books by wiping with a damp cloth soaked in vinegar. Then wipe again with plain water.
- Wash cloth books in the washing machine, adding ½ cup vinegar to the rinse cycle to disinfect.
- Put 1 teaspoon baking soda in warm water in the bathroom sink. Soak baby combs and brushes, then rinse and dry.
- To clean and deodorize cloth diapers, soak them in 2 quarts warm water and ½ cup baking soda for 1 hour before washing. Then wash as usual.
- Neutralize smells in the diaper pail by sprinkling baking soda on dirty diapers.

GARDENING

"The person who sows seeds of kindness will have a perpetual harvest."
—Amish proverb

Lancaster County, Pennsylvania, where many Amish people live, is considered one of the most productive agricultural areas in the world. That's partially due to the way the Amish tend to the earth: They use natural, economical methods developed over centuries. Eating what they grow is cost-effective and keeps them healthy, as does the hard physical work.

SEED SAVING

The Amish save seeds from the biggest and strongest plants in their gardens and fields to use for planting the next season. This practice not only saves money but lets them keep heirloom varieties alive. They plant only species that are tasty and nutritious and that can be canned, dried, or eaten fresh, rather than varieties that can keep for months on a store shelf. The seeds must be carefully dried and stored over the winter, away from moisture, light, and heat.

To save your seeds:

- Allow plants or flowers to go to seed. On a dry day when the seeds are mature, gather them before they begin to scatter.
- Some of the easiest seeds to collect are marigolds, bachelor's buttons, sunflowers, lettuce, radishes, corn, and beans. Pumpkin and squash seeds can be collected after opening the gourds.
- Different kinds of seeds will need different preparation. Some, like marigolds, come from the plant in discrete clumps that can easily be spread out to dry. Just make sure that each seed has a little space around it. Other seeds, like those from gourds and watermelons, are embedded in mushy plant material that needs to be removed. Rinse off the seeds with water, using your hands to pull off the mushy part as quickly as you can. Do not soak the seeds in water or they will begin to germinate. Pat the seeds dry

before placing them between the layers of paper towels or clean newspaper for final drying.

- When the seeds feel entirely dry, store them in a glass jar or paper envelope in a cool, dry place over the winter.
- Make sure that you grow zucchini far away from pumpkins because those two vegetables can cross-pollinate. The fruits and vegetables will be fine, but the seeds will carry traits of both plants. Hot peppers and sweet peppers also cross-pollinate and their seeds, too, will be unpredictable.

CREATING GOOD SOIL

If your garden has not been used in several years, or if it has been overused, try the following:

- In late fall, plow the garden and sow ryegrass. In spring, turn the ryegrass under to enrich the soil. Then plow and plant as usual.
- If the soil is poor, plant only beans the first year. They will put nitrogen back in the soil.

STARTING SEEDS

Start your seeds indoors in peat pots about six to eight weeks before you want to plant outside. Provide a strong light source, like a hanging fluorescent light, at least 12 hours a day. About a week before transplanting the plants, start taking them outside for part of each day to "harden them off."

- Transplant when three or four leaves appear on the stem.
- If plants grow too fast and start to get spindly, you can slow their growth by putting them in a cooler place.

PLANTING TIPS

- Plant crops that bear fruit above ground as the moon is increasing in size from the new moon to the full moon.
- However, plant crops that bear fruit below ground as the moon is decreasing in size, from the full moon to the dark of the moon.
- Plant potatoes, peas, and lettuce near St. Patrick's Day.
- Plant onion sets, lettuce, and radishes early—one to two months before the last frost.
- Set out broccoli, cauliflower, and cabbage at least one month before the last frost in your area.
- Plant tomatoes, corn, beans, squash, melons, basil, sunflowers, and other frost-sensitive plants only after the last frost in your area.
- Plant basil next to tomato plants to enhance flavor.

God-given Gifts

The basic thing which gives me a sense of well-being is a garden to provide me with my year's supply of food and decoration. From there I can have all the produce canned and put away, and a supply of the herbs I need to heal and beautify, dried and stored away in labeled jars.

—Emma Byler, *Plain and Happy Living*

- Plant dill among cucumbers and squash to enhance flavor and deter bugs and beetles.

INSECT CONTROL

- Plant a row of marigolds around the garden to discourage insects.
- Pour a dipper of soapy water at the base of each plant to keep bugs away. To get rid of aphids and mealy bugs, spray leaves, including the undersides, with a solution of liquid soap and water, using about 1 tablespoon soap to 1 gallon water.
- Make a strong tea of catnip, thyme, sage, or hyssop, and spray directly onto plants.
- Soak tobacco in water to make a tea that will repel insects, and use it on the ground around plants—except for tomatoes.
- To get rid of slugs and snails, sprinkle salt on them.
- Spray broccoli, cauliflower, and cabbage with a solution of 1 cup salt to 1 gallon water once or twice a week to discourage worms and other insects.
- To get rid of aphids, spray leaves with a solution of onion and garlic (mashed or blended) with water. Be sure to spray the bottom side of the leaves.
- Dust plants for worms using a mixture of 4 cups flour to 1 tablespoon baking soda.
- Put bluebird houses near the garden to encourage bluebird nesting. Bluebirds eat mainly insects.

- Hang gourds for nests for purple martins, which eat large numbers of insects.
- Bats eat ⅓ their weight in insects nightly during the warm months. If they do not have habitat, put up a bat house.

OTHER PESTS

- To keep birds from eating berries or tomatoes, tie pieces of cloth to sticks and set them upright in the ground. When the wind blows, the motion of the cloth will frighten them.
- Plant a row of onions all around the garden to discourage rabbits and deer from eating your plants.
- To keep dogs and other animals out of flower beds, sprinkle cayenne pepper on the beds.
- To keep deer away from your garden, spread something with human scent, like hair clippings, around the edge, or hang it in paper bags in the trees nearby. Deer will avoid anything that smells human.

TIPS FOR WORKING IN THE GARDEN

- Pull or hoe weeds away from the plants you are growing.
- Hoe the earth between rows to keep it loose to help plants grow and to deter weeds.
- To keep flowers blooming: Dissolve 1 package plain gelatin (not flavored Jell-O) in 3 cups hot water; cool, then apply to flowers.
- Water flowers with a solution of 3 tablespoons peroxide to 1 gallon water.

 To help lilacs bloom, spread a cup of Epsom salts around the base just as the plant is beginning to bud. In the fall, spread Epsom salts around your spring-blooming bushes, such as azaleas.

 When tomato plants get big, mulch around them with straw. Tie the main parts of the plant to a 4- to 5-foot-long stake.

 To get rid of weeds in particular places, pour boiling water on them.

Garden Lore

- If you want to get rid of briars or thistles, cut them on St. John's Day in mid-August.
- If a fruit tree won't bear fruit, drive a nail into it.
- When transplanting trees, determine which side of each tree is facing south before you dig them up. When you transfer them to their new locations, make sure that the side that was facing south is planted facing south again. Maintaining the same orientation to the directions helps the tree continue to grow well.

STORING YOUR BOUNTY

Keep root crops (like carrots, turnips, beets) for use throughout the winter by placing them in a clean bucket, then filling it with sand. Cover the bucket to keep out light, and store it in a cool, dry place like a basement or root cellar.

 Gather herbs in the morning just after the dew has dried. Hang them up to dry in a cool, dry place where the air circulates. After a day or two, crumble the dried herbs and keep them in glass jars over the winter.

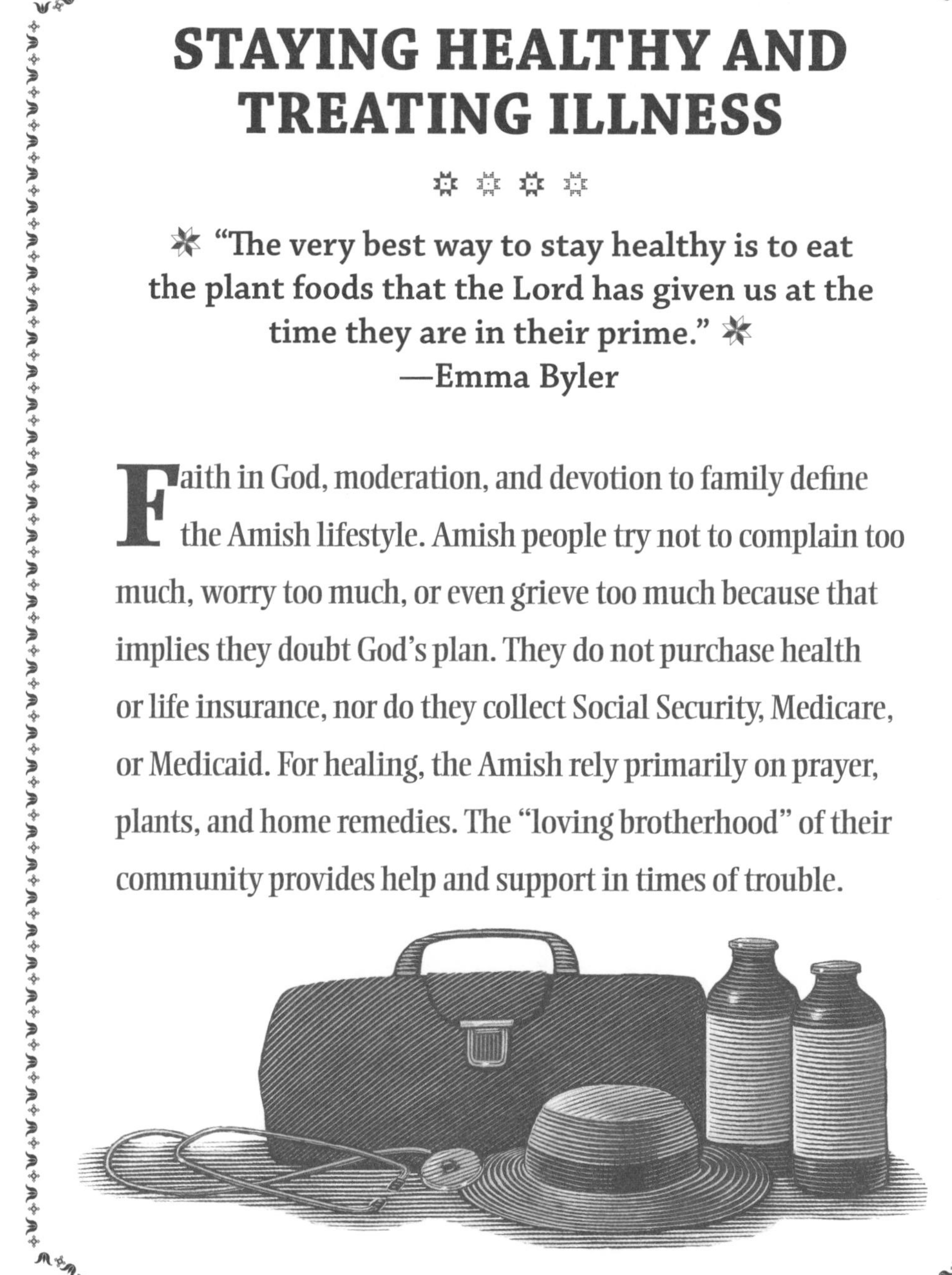

STAYING HEALTHY AND TREATING ILLNESS

"The very best way to stay healthy is to eat the plant foods that the Lord has given us at the time they are in their prime."
—Emma Byler

Faith in God, moderation, and devotion to family define the Amish lifestyle. Amish people try not to complain too much, worry too much, or even grieve too much because that implies they doubt God's plan. They do not purchase health or life insurance, nor do they collect Social Security, Medicare, or Medicaid. For healing, the Amish rely primarily on prayer, plants, and home remedies. The "loving brotherhood" of their community provides help and support in times of trouble.

AMISH REMEDIES

Allergies

For the runny nose and sinus congestion associated with hay fever, sniff salt water into your nose and your sinuses to clear out pollen, dust, and mucus. Put ½ teaspoon salt in 8 ounces warm water (preferably filtered, unchlorinated). Hold one side of your nose shut and gently inhale through the other nostril. Hold your breath for ten seconds, then blow it back out. Repeat on the other side. **Caution:** Do not swallow or inhale the salt water into your lungs.

Anxiety

- Sit in a quiet place and repeat the 23rd Psalm.
- Share a scalp, back, or foot massage with a friend or family member.
- Drink a cup of peppermint (*Mentha piperita*) tea.
- Drink a cup of catnip (*Nepeta cataria*) tea at bedtime.
- Avoid caffeine! A cup of herb tea can't overcome the nervousness created by several cups of coffee or an energy drink.

Athlete's Foot

- Soak your feet every night in a mixture of 1 cup vinegar and 2 quarts water. Dry thoroughly.
- Sprinkle baking soda in between your shoes.
- Change socks twice a day.
- To relieve itching and kill the fungus, apply fresh crushed jewelweed (*Impatiens capensis*) to clean, dry feet.

Bites and Stings

- To prevent chigger bites, put sprigs of pennyroyal (*Hedeoma pulegioides*) in your socks.
- Wash a bite with salt water.
- Rub a bite with fresh jewelweed (*Impatiens capensis*). Apply several times per day for two to three days to stop itching.
- Crush 2 to 3 plantain leaves (*Plantago major* and *Plantago minor*), and rub together. Apply to the bite as a poultice and leave on for 15 to 20 minutes. Repeat as needed. *Note*: This is the weedy perennial, which grows all over North America, not the tropical fruit called plantain that looks like a banana.
- Cut an onion in half and hold it on the bite or sting for 5 to 10 minutes immediately after being bitten or stung. Then discard.

- Dab vinegar directly on the bite to stop itching.
- Rub a bar of soap on the bite to stop itching.

Bladder or Urinary Tract Infections

- Drink as much cranberry juice as you can at the first symptoms.
- Make a tea from fresh corn silk (*Zea mays*) when in season. Use ⅔ cup corn silk to 1 quart water. Pour boiling water onto the corn silk, cool, and strain. Drink 1 cup three times a day for 7 to 10 days.
- Watermelon seed tea will flush the system. Put ⅛ cup fresh watermelon seeds in a pint jar and fill with boiling water. Cool, strain, and drink 1 pint per day for ten days.

A Godly Life

The Amish believe that spiritual health is more important than physical health. Here are some of the principles they follow.

Rules of a Godly Life

Be friendly to all and a burden to no one. Live holy before God; before yourself, moderately; before your neighbors, honestly. Let your life be modest and reserved, your manner courteous, your admonitions friendly, your forgiveness willing, your promises true, your speech wise, and share gladly the bounties you receive.

—*Ernsthafte Christenpflicht,* 1793

- Use the leaves or root of dandelion (*Taraxacum officinale*) as a diuretic to flush the bladder and kidneys. Put 1 teaspoon dried dandelion leaves in a cup and add 1 cup boiling water. Steep for five minutes. Drink 2 to 3 cups per day.

Bolstering Immunity

Spring tonics and blood purifiers have long been used by the Amish to cleanse the system and get the blood moving again after the sluggishness of winter. Though this practice is not recognized by Western medicine, the ingredients in Amish tonics and blood purifiers are chock-full of vitamins and minerals—and some of the plants have been found to stimulate the immune system.

- Beets purify and build up the blood. Mix 1 cup beet juice with 2 cups red grape juice. Store in the refrigerator and take 1 tablespoon three or four times daily for two weeks.

- Put 1 ounce burdock root (*Arctium lappa*) in 1 pint water and boil gently for 15 minutes. Strain, cool, and drink three to four times daily until it is gone.

- Take 1 cup red clover (*Trifolium pratense*) tea once a day for one week. Red clover is high in calcium, magnesium, and potassium. **Caution:** Red clover can thin the blood, so do not use if you are pregnant or if you are taking aspirin or blood thinners.

Burns

- Put the burned skin under cool running water. Pat dry. Cut off part of an aloe vera leaf and squeeze the sap onto the affected skin. **Caution:** Seek medical attention for second- or third-degree burns (if you have blisters, redness and swelling, white or blackened skin, or numbness).

- Run cool water on the burn, then cover the area with honey and a sterile gauze. Change the dressing several times a day. Honey draws water out of the burned tissues and prevents the growth of bacteria.

Herbal Medicine

Many Amish remedies use herbs for healing. Plants are found in their fields, woods, and fencerows, or they are grown around their houses. Herbal medicine dates back thousands of years, and many of today's prescription medicines are derived from plants and their constituents, either natural or synthetic. Many over-the-counter medicines are based on plants, too, including aspirin, whose constituents are found in willow bark. **Caution:** Do not use plants for medicine unless you are sure you have correctly identified the plant.

Cold and Congestion

- Boil 1 tablespoon dried peppermint leaves in 1 quart water for about one minute. Remove from heat, and let cool a few minutes. Put a towel over your head and the pan, and inhale the steam.

Constipation

- Exercise, drink 8 glasses of water daily, and eat high-fiber foods.
- Eat ½ ounce sesame seed (no more) daily and drink lots of water.

Cough

- Sauté 6 finely chopped white onions (*Allium cepa*) in 2 tablespoons olive oil until transparent. Add 1 cup honey and the juice of 1 lemon, cooking over low heat until the mixture thickens. Take 1 tablespoon every half hour or as needed for coughs. **Caution:** Do not give honey to children under two years of age. It can be fatal. Substitute 1 cup brown sugar.
- Make a hot toddy with whiskey, fresh lemon juice, and honey. Drink and go to bed to "sweat out" the illness under the covers.

Herbal Tea

Herbs make delicious and therapeutic teas. These are the basics of herbal tea preparation:

- Use about 1 teaspoon fresh or dried leaves from the plant—more if it's fresh, less if it's dried. Put the herb into your teacup or teapot and pour 1 cup boiling water on it. Let it sit—this is called "steeping"—for about 5 minutes, then drink.
- The bark or roots must boil longer to extract the medicinal qualities. Use a small handful of bark or roots to 1 quart water in a stainless steel, glass, or enamel pan. Boil 5 to 10 minutes, then strain. Some herbs interact with copper, nonstick coatings, and aluminum, creating toxic compounds.

- Use a mustard plaster to help relieve a chest cold and bronchitis. Mix 1 tablespoon dry mustard with 4 tablespoons flour and enough water to make a runny paste. Spread the mixture on a square of muslin. Put olive oil on the patient's chest, and then apply the mustard plaster. Leave it on long enough to warm the area. Watch carefully because the plaster gets very hot and can burn the skin.

- To soothe an irritated and raw throat, mix together 2 tablespoons dried horehound (*Marrubium vulgare*) and 1 ounce slippery elm bark (*Ulmas fulva*). Add 1 pint boiling water and steep. Sweeten as desired. Take 1 tablespoon at a time. **Caution:** Do not sweeten with honey for young children, as honey can cause a fatal reaction.

- For a cough suppressant, put 1 tablespoon dried cherry bark (*Prunus serotina*) and 1 pint water in a stainless steel, glass, or enamel pan. Boil 5 to 10 minutes. (**Caution:** This must be boiled to make it nontoxic!) Drink ¼ cup five times a day for no more than three days. **Caution:** Should not be used by children under 12 or pregnant women. Adults should not exceed the recommended dose.

Depression

- Get plenty of exercise and fresh air. Make sure you are getting the vitamins you need, especially if you were pregnant recently.

- Try Saint-John's-wort (*Hypericum perforatum*). Make tea with 1 to 2 teaspoons of the dried herb and drink twice daily. **Caution:** Pregnant women and children under the age of 18 should not use this remedy.

- Count your blessings. Spend some time every day being thankful for what you have.

"Be contented, and do not try to catch up with the world's uneasiness and speed."
—Amish motto

Diarrhea

- Use any part of the blackberry plant (*Rubus hispidus*). Steep 1 teaspoon dried leaves in 1 cup hot water for 10 to 15 minutes; drink several times a day. Make unripe blackberry fruits into a jelly to use during the winter, or dig up blackberry roots for wintertime use. Blackberry jelly or even 1 to 2 ounces of blackberry wine can be used instead of tea.

Earache

- Gather mullein flowers (*Verbascum thapsus*) when in bloom. Steep in a small jar of olive oil for several days. Strain out the flowers. When needed, warm a few drops and put them into the ear with an eyedropper.

Fever

Fever is a symptom, not a disease. However, there are many remedies to break a fever that involve drinking herb tea and then "sweating out" the disease.

- Steep ½ ounce elderberry flowers (*Sambucus nigra*) in 1 quart boiling water for 15 minutes, then strain. Drink 1 cup every four hours, up to 4 cups a day. Immediately after drinking the tea, go to bed and pile on blankets to "sweat out" the disease.

- Steep 2 teaspoons dried strawberry leaves (*Fragaria spp.*) in 1 cup boiling water. Follow the instructions above.

Flu

- At the first sign of flu (sudden fever over 101 degrees Fahrenheit, aches, and pains), take 1 cup boneset (*Eupatorium perfoliatum*) tea and go to bed. Take no more than 1 cup per day or you will feel worse. **Caution:** Pregnant women should avoid this remedy.

Gas

- To dispel gas, ease stomach cramps, and aid digestion, chew a small handful (about 1 tablespoon) anise (*Pimpinella anisum*), caraway (*Carum carvi*), or fennel seeds (*Foeniculum vulgare*) after a meal.

Headache

- Crush fresh rosemary or sage and rub on temples and forehead. Discard the crushed plant after rubbing it on your skin.
- Soak a handkerchief in vinegar. Wring out and put on forehead, lie down, and relax for 15 minutes.

Heartburn and Indigestion

- Make a ginger tea by stirring ½ teaspoon ginger into 1 cup boiling water. Drink up to 3 or 4 cups per day. **Caution:** Pregnant women, people with diabetes, and people with heart conditions should not use this.
- Drink peppermint tea after every meal. Use 1 teaspoon dried peppermint to 1 cup boiling water.
- Eat smaller amounts, more slowly, and relax.
- Drink at least 8 glasses of water daily.
- Eat a small handful of anise seed, caraway seed, or fennel seed to dispel gas and indigestion.

Insomnia

- Drink 1 cup catnip tea or peppermint tea before bedtime.
- Drink 1 cup warm milk before bedtime.
- For restful sleep, you need a tired body and a good conscience.

- One hour of sleep before midnight is worth two hours sleep after midnight.

Itching

The following remedies only relieve the symptoms of itching, not the cause—which can be insect bites, allergic reactions, dry skin, poison ivy, prescription drugs, or certain conditions of the thyroid, kidneys, or blood. It's best to treat the cause of the itching to achieve more complete relief.

- Make an oatmeal poultice or take an oatmeal bath. Use oatmeal straight from the box—preferably instant oatmeal because it dissoves quickly. Just make sure it has no flavorings or additives.
- Dab some vinegar onto the affected areas; let it dry on the skin.
- Catnip (*Nepeta cataria*) and peppermint tea (*Mentha piperita*) contain menthol, which relieves itching and cools the skin. Make a tea of either herb, and apply it to the skin. Air dry.
- Apply aloe vera—either sap from a leaf of the plant or gel purchased over the counter—directly to the itch.
- To treat dry skin, use a moisturizer. The Amish make homemade lotions using glycerin and rose water, cocoa butter, or olive oil.

Muscle Sprains and Strains

- For the first few days after the injury, apply ice or cold packs. Then apply heat.
- Soak in a bath of Epsom salts and hot water.
- Make a poultice of plantain (*Plantago major*) leaves. Gather several handfuls, chop, and put about ¾ cup into a bowl; pour 1 cup boiling water over it. Let steep about 15 minutes. Apply to injured area for about 20 minutes at a time for several days.
- Use a poultice of comfrey (*Symphytum officinale*). Gather several handfuls, chop, and steep in boiling water. Apply to injured area—either directly or contained in a piece of cotton toweling—for about 20 minutes at a time for several days.

Nausea and Vomiting

- If pregnant, drink raspberry leaf (*Rubus idaeus*) tea. Use 1 teaspoon raspberry leaf to 1 cup boiling water.
- Peppermint reduces the gag reflex and helps to quell vomiting. Make a peppermint (*Mentha piperita*) tea, using 1 teaspoon dried leaf to 1 cup boiling water. Let cool, then sip slowly.

Pain

- Cayenne pepper (*Capsicum spp.*) used externally can relieve pain, especially from muscle aches and strains and arthritis. Heat 1 cup vinegar in a stainless steel or glass pan. Add

1 tablespoon cayenne pepper and simmer gently. Apply with a cloth. **Caution:** Do not apply to eyes or mucous membranes or touch those parts with your hands until you have washed your hands thoroughly. Cayenne causes intense burning.

Good Samaritan Salve

This recipe has been used by Amish people for generations, and they tell stories about its healing powers for bites, muscle sprains and strains, and wounds.

¼ ounce oil of wintergreen
¼ ounce oil of cinnamon
¼ ounce oil of lavender
¼ ounce oil of sassafras (or ½ ounce sassafras leaves)
1 ounce camphor
1 quart raw linseed oil

Combine and rub on the affected area. **Caution:** Some herbalists warn against using wintergreen because of its toxic effects.

- Meadowsweet (*Filipendula ulmaria*) contains aspirin-related compounds. Mix 1 teaspoon dried meadowsweet in 1 cup boiling water, cover, and let steep five minutes. Use no more than 1 cup every four hours. **Caution:** Do not use if you are allergic to aspirin. It can cause the same allergic reaction as an aspirin tablet.

Prostate

- Amish men use corn silk (*Zea mays*) to help lessen the symptoms of an enlarged prostate. Cut the silk from 6 ears of fresh corn. Bring 1 quart water to boil, put the silk in the water, return to a boil, and simmer for 10 minutes. Strain and drink. Drink 2 glasses of water first thing every morning and 3 cups corn silk tea a day for one week. Corn silk can also be dried for use in the wintertime.

- Watermelon seed (*Citrullis citrullis*) tea is a diuretic used for kidney and bladder problems, as well as for prostate issues. Place ⅛ cup watermelon seeds in a glass pint jar and cover with boiling water. Strain and drink after the tea has cooled. Drink 1 pint every day for ten days.

- Saw palmetto (*Serenoa repens*) is well-known as a remedy for prostate problems. Take it in capsules.

Skin Ulcers and Sores

- Apply aloe vera, honey, or vitamin E oil.

- Apply a tea from goldenseal (*Hydrastis canadensis*).

Sore Throat

- Cut a peeled garlic clove in half. Put ½ in your mouth and suck as if it were a cough drop. Or, peel a garlic clove and chew it raw.

- Gargle with 2 tablespoons goldenseal (*Hydrastis canadensis*) tea; swallow it.) *Note*: This plant is endangered in many areas. You can grow it yourself or substitute Oregon grape root (*Mahonia aquafolium*) or barberry (*Berberis vulgaris*), which contain the same effective compounds but are not endangered.

- Gargle with ½ cup horehound (*Marrubium vulgare*) tea as needed; do not swallow. Horehound cough drops are also effective.

- Gargle with ¼ cup sage tea (*Salvia officinalis*) up to four times per day. Sage relieves pain and swelling and also kills viruses and bacteria. **Caution:** Pregnant women should not use this herb. If used medicinally, it will reduce milk flow in breastfeeding women. However, sage can be used as seasoning. **Caution:** Strep throat should be diagnosed and treated with antibiotics to prevent rheumatic fever, a complication of untreated or poorly treated strep throat that can permanently damage the heart.

Wounds and Cuts

- Crush plantain leaves (*Plantago major* and *Plantago minor*) and apply directly to the wound several times a day.

- Pour vinegar on a clean cloth and apply to the wound, pressing until bleeding stops. Pour a small amount of vinegar on a piece of clean brown paper and apply to the wound to encourage clotting.

- Crush fresh yarrow leaves (*Achillea millefolium*) and apply directly to the wound three to four times daily.

To avoid sickness, never pay the doctor in full!

Brauche or Powwowing

Brauche is the term for a type of magical, spiritual healing practice among the Pennsylvania Dutch Amish. The Algonquin Indians also had a spiritual healing tradition, and the word they used for it sounded like "powwow" to European immigrants. When speaking about "brauching" in English, the Amish will often refer to it as "powwowing." They also may refer to it as "calling a blessing" because they are asking for God's intervention.

Brauchers, or powwow doctors, use their charms to cure all kinds of symptoms and ailments, including burns, pain, bleeding, warts, headaches, and earaches. For example, to remove a wart, a braucher would say a specific prayer, rub half a potato on the wart, and bury the potato. The patient would be told: "As the potato rots away, your wart will go away."

Many people claim to have been healed of serious illnesses by these methods. In the Amish newspaper *The Budget*, letters to the editor still describe and debate this tradition.

PERSONAL CARE AND MORE

"Start each day with a fresh beginning as if this whole world was made anew."
—Amish motto

The Amish call themselves "plain folk"—and they are true to the term. They shun graven images and mirrors, dress in a few solid colors, and do not style their hair or wear makeup. Amish children's dolls have no faces. Individualism, vanity, and greed are the enemy of their community and lifestyle. Living a life pleasing to God does require attention to personal care and health, however, and the Amish have developed an abundance of simple and effective personal-care practices.

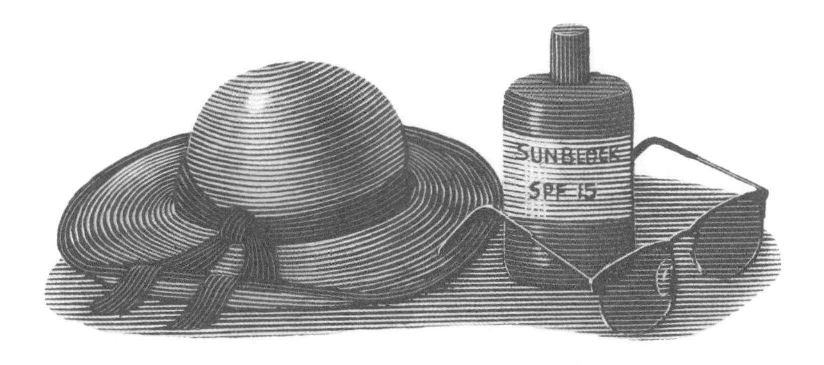

BABY CARE

- For constipation, mix ½ teaspoon olive oil into the baby's regular food *no more than once a day*, until the bowels become regular. **Caution:** Check first with the baby's physician before trying this remedy.

Homemade Baby Wipes

These wipes are very economical! Combine the following in an empty wipes box or plastic container:

1½ tablespoons baby shampoo
1½ tablespoons baby oil
1½ tablespoons witch hazel or rubbing alcohol
2½ cups hot water

- Shake until all ingredients are combined.
- Cut a roll of paper towels in half. You can use a long sharp kitchen knife or heavy-duty kitchen shears. Use sturdy paper towels, not the flimsy ones.
- Put the paper towels in the wipes box. Soak, turning several times, until liquid is absorbed.
- Tear off a section at a time to use as baby wipes.

- For diaper rash or rash on baby's face, apply plain yogurt.

- For diaper rash or chapped skin, rub a little vegetable oil into the affected area.

- For cradle cap, rub olive oil into the baby's scalp. Leave for several hours, then shampoo with a gentle soap, rinse, and pat dry.

- For eczema, keep your baby's skin moisturized all the time and make sure he or she is drinking plenty of liquids. Moisturize with olive oil to which a little fresh aloe vera has been mixed in.

DIET

Weight Loss

- Eat breakfast every day.
- Don't eat anything after 7 p.m.
- Mix 1 tablespoon apple cider vinegar and 1 tablespoon honey into a glass of warm water. Drink the mixture 15 to 20 minutes before eating to quell your appetite.
- Eat lots of fresh lettuce in the spring and summer. Eat lots of soup in the fall and winter.

Walk Like the Amish

The average Amish man takes more than 18,000 steps every day, and the average Amish woman takes about 14,000 steps. As a result, only 4 percent of Amish people are obese compared to 31 percent of the U.S. population. Their day includes lots of physical labor, and they walk almost everywhere.

- If dieting is difficult for you, or your weight has gone up and down a lot, try dieting every other day.
- Some Amish people practice short fasts as described in the Bible. They believe this purifies the body and gives your system a chance to cleanse itself. Go 1 whole day without eating, but drink plenty of water. Do this once a week.

- Do a fruit fast for a day. Eat only fresh fruit and drink water. (Avoid fruit juice unless you squeeze it yourself because it often has extra sugar or preservatives in it.)
- Do a "watermelon fast" for a day. Eat only refreshing watermelon, drink plenty of water, and find yourself refreshed!
- Eat lightly after fasting or you will feel sick and might regain the weight you lost.

Caution: Do not fast if you have diabetes, or are pregnant or breastfeeding. Consult your doctor before fasting if you have a serious medical condition.

Amish weight loss advice: "Do push ups. Just push up from the table!"

MOUTH CARE

Breath

- To make a mouthwash, mix 1 teaspoon baking soda with 1 cup water. Add 1 or 2 drops peppermint extract and stir. Rinse your mouth and gargle. (You can buy peppermint extract in the baking section of the grocery store.)
- Chew fresh parsley to dispel odors.
- Chew a few coffee beans to freshen the breath.

Dentures

- Mix 1 teaspoon baking soda and 1 cup hot water. Soak dentures in the solution for 30 minutes. Brush dentures and rinse.

Teeth

- Use baking soda to brush teeth. Dip a damp toothbrush into a small container of baking soda, then brush and rinse.

- Mix together equal amounts of baking soda and salt to make toothpaste.

- Mix ½ cup baking soda, ½ cup salt, and a few drops of peppermint oil to make toothpaste.

- Mix enough peroxide with baking soda to make a paste. Use immediately to brush teeth, whiten teeth, and kill bacteria.

SKIN CARE

Chapped Hands

This mild, moisturizing soap will help heal your chapped hands. Because you are starting with soap that is already made, you don't have to use lye to make this recipe.

- Melt 1 pound solid, mild, unscented hand soap. Stir in 8 ounces honey. Add 1 beaten egg yolk and ⅛ cup Borax (not boric acid). Melt and stir together. If you'd like some fragrance, add essential oils like rose geranium, lavender, peppermint, or lemongrass while the mixture is still warm but not completely set. Then pour the soap into a 1-quart glass pan or into molds to make individual bars of soap. Let set for 24 hours, then cut into individual cakes of soap. Stack so that air can circulate around them and let them harden for another 24 hours. Wrap them in waxed paper or plastic wrap to keep them fresh, or just stack them on a shelf.

- Make the soap into special shapes by using cookie cutters. Set them on waxed paper on a cookie sheet and pour 1 to 2 inches of soap into them. Let set until hard, then remove the cookie cutter. Soap will slide out.

Chapped Lips

- Use pure lanolin, a natural and very powerful moisturizer that comes from sheep's wool. It has a consistency like petroleum jelly and can be rubbed directly on the skin.

- Use sweet oil or olive oil on chapped lips several times a day.

Deodorant

- After bathing, rub underarms with vinegar.

- Lavender deodorant: Boil 1 pint vinegar in a glass or stainless steel pan. Add ½ cup lavender flowers or 5 drops lavender essential oil; let cool. Strain, then store in a glass jar. Pour a small amount on a towel and rub on underarms after bathing. *Note*: If you prefer another scent, try peppermint, sage, or rosemary.

Sunburn

- Bathe the sunburned area in cool water immediately. Apply vinegar with a soft cloth, and let it dry on the skin. The vinegar will cool it and prevent itching. Reapply it as needed, once or twice a day.

- After bathing the area in cool water, apply aloe vera sap from the plant directly on the sunburn and let it dry on the skin. Repeat several times daily. Or, use store-bought pure aloe vera gel (not lotion with aloe vera added to it).

HAIR CARE

Dandruff

- Rub warm coconut oil into the scalp before shampooing. Wrap hair in a towel and leave the oil on it for 20 to 30 minutes. Then shampoo with gentle soap.

- Rinse hair with tea made from burdock leaves (*Arctium lappa*). Put 1 quart water in a glass, stainless steel, or enamel pot and bring to a boil. Add 4 teaspoons burdock leaves. Let steep for 10 minutes, then strain out the plant material, and apply the burdock tea to hair. Leave on for about 10 minutes, then rinse with plain warm water.

- Sage tea, as described on the next page, can also help eliminate dandruff.

Hair Rinse and Conditioner

- To make hair shiny and bring out natural highlights, make this conditioner to use whenever you want. In a bowl, beat 1 egg very well. Add 1 cup lukewarm water (not too hot or you will cook the egg!). Apply to hair after shampooing, then rinse out.

- Make 2 cups sage (*Salvia officinalis*) tea, using about 4 teaspoons dried sage to 1 quart boiling water. Steep 10 minutes, then strain. Apply the whole quart to your hair, and massage the tea into your scalp. Wrap hair in a towel and relax for 10 minutes, then rinse with plain warm water. This promotes healthy hair and has a pleasant, mild herbal scent.

- After shampooing, rinse hair with 1 tablespoon vinegar that's been stirred into a glass of warm water. This eliminates any buildup from hair products and leaves it soft and shiny. If you use apple cider vinegar, it will leave a pleasant smell.

Shampoo

- Use pure liquid castile soap for shampoo.

- If you prefer, add a few drops of your favorite essential oil to bottle soap: lavender, rose geranium, and lemongrass work well.